Introduction

The questions in this book will help you to prepare for your Standard Grade Physical Education examination.

Examination areas

✔ The areas involved in the different questions are:

1. *Activities* – including different roles, qualities needed, scoring systems, tactics, rules and codes of conduct

2. *The Body in Action* – including different aspects of physical fitness, and principles and methods of training

3. *Skills and Techniques* – including ways of practising and learning different skills.

The questions in this book are set out in this order.

✔ Answers are provided in the centre section. These pages are removable.

✔ To help you in your revision, the answer section shows you which questions are Foundation level, which are General level and which are Credit level. The following system is used:

> Answers to Foundation level questions are printed on a plain background (like this).
> Answers to General level questions are printed on a hatched background (like this).
> Answers to Credit level questions are printed on a shaded background (like this).

You should attempt all the questions. Check with your teacher, however, about which levels you are sitting in the examination.

✔ Spend time revising each topic and then try the questions on that topic. To help you with your revision, we recommend that you obtain a copy of Leckie & Leckie's other Standard Grade Physical Education book, *Standard Grade Physical Education Course Notes*, from your school or bookshop.

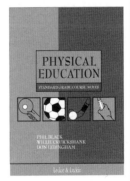

At the foot of every page of questions, you will find a page reference to Leckie & Leckie's *Standard Grade Physical Education Course Notes*. Look up these pages for help with answering the questions.

Advice on answering examination questions

✔ **Different types of information**
  - The elements 'Evaluating' and 'Knowledge and Understanding' are tested in each question at each level. Parts (a) and (b) of each question test 'Evaluating' – they are based directly on the video you watch. Parts (c) and (d) test your 'Knowledge and Understanding'.

  - **Evaluating** questions ask you to **observe** and **describe** action, **make judgements** about what a performer has done well and, where necessary, **suggest improvements**.

  - **Knowledge and Understanding** questions ask you to **show knowledge** of and then **apply** relevant facts and principles.

✔ **Different types of questions**
The ways in which questions are asked in this book are similar to the ways in which questions will be asked in your actual examination. Many different types of question format are used.

Occasionally, you will be asked to answer questions that require little writing. For example, you will complete tick boxes, complete grids and fill in missing words in sentences.

On other occasions, you will write a few sentences where you explain and offer different examples to show your understanding.

Here is an example of an Evaluating question in question parts (a) and (b):

(a) Describe, in the correct order, four movements of the attacking player.

  (i) _____

  (ii) _____

  (iii) _____

  (iv) _____

(b) Suggest two improvements the attacker could make to improve her chance of scoring.

  (i) _____

  (ii) _____

In the video examination, you will see many different activities being performed. Some of these activities may not be in your Standard Grade course. Remember that the questions are asking about general details of physical activity which you will have experienced in your course.

The questions are about:

- *Activities*
- *The Body in Action*
- *Skills and Techniques*

with pull-out answer section

KIRKLAND HIGH SCHOOL
AND
COMMUNITY COLLEGE

QUESTIONS in STANDARD GRADE PHYSICAL EDUCATION

MALCOLM THORBURN

Copyright © 1999 Malcolm Thorburn

All rights reserved. No part of this publication may be stored in a retrieval system, or transmitted in any form or by any means, electronic, mechanical, photocopying, recording or otherwise, without prior permission in writing from Leckie & Leckie (Publishers). Legal action will be taken by Leckie & Leckie against any infringement of our copyright.

ISBN 1-898890-66-8

Published by
Leckie & Leckie
8 Whitehill Terrace
St Andrews
Scotland
KY16 8RN
Tel. 01334 475656
Fax. 01334 477392
email: s.leckie@leckie-and-leckie.co.uk
web: www.leckie-and-leckie.co.uk

Edited by Willie Cruickshank

Special thanks to
Bruce Ryan (page make-up), Hamish Sanderson (illustration) and
Emily Dewhurst (production assistance)

Printed in Scotland by Inglis Allen on environmentally-friendly paper. The paper is made from a mixture of sawmill waste, forest thinnings and wood from sustainable forests.

Leckie & Leckie

Contents

1. Activities

Types of activity

Key points ✔ There are many different types of activities:
- individual, team and group
- competitive and non-competitive
- indirectly competitive and directly competitive.

✔ There are many reasons for participation in different activities:
- social, physical, health and personal.

1. Some activities can only be performed either individually (e.g. squash) or as part of a team or group (e.g. lacrosse). Other activities can be performed both on your own and as part of a team (e.g. tennis).

   Tick the correct boxes in the table below for these different activities.

Activity	Individual Activity	Team/Group Activity
Basketball		
Social dancing		
Marathon running		
4 x 400 m relay		
Badminton		
800 m	.	

2. Activities can be competitive, non-competitive or both.
   (i) What does competitive mean?
   (ii) What does non-competitive mean?

3. There are many reasons why people participate in activities – reasons can be social, physical, health or personal in nature. Match each of the following descriptions to a different reason for participation:

physical	social	health	personal

'I enjoy getting out and meeting other people. We all take part together and then go out afterwards.'	
'I like the challenge. I need the thrill of competing against myself when I am rock climbing.'	
'Regular exercise is good for me. It is not too difficult, but demanding enough to help me to live a long and healthy life.'	
'Swimming is my favourite sport. The longer events are great for my endurance and the sprint events are great for improving power.'	

4. Copy and complete the table below. Use your experience of different activities in your answer. Your main reasons for participation should include reference to one social, one physical, one health and one personal benefit. An example answer is provided.

Type of activity	Activity chosen	Your main reason for participation
Team, directly competitive	Football	Social – I enjoy being part of a team. We have trained and played together for many years and all get on well together.
Team, directly competitive		
Individual, indirectly competitive		
Team, indirectly competitive		
Individual, non-competitive		

5. Participation levels in activities can be affected by different factors. Age is one factor that affects levels of active participation.

   Choose two different activities, one in which you are most likely to participate at a younger age and one in which participation can be lifelong. Explain why age is a factor in each.

Younger age activity:	Explanation:
Lifelong activity:	Explanation:

6. Other factors, such as **money**, **weather**, **facilities** and **disability**, can affect participation levels in certain activities. Choose two of these factors and explain how each is significant in either helping or reducing levels of participation. An example answer is provided.

Activity: Cross-country running	Factor chosen: Money
Explanation: Cross-country running is quite inexpensive. There are many places you can run free of charge. Apart from the cost of correct training shoes, there are few other costs for a recreational runner.	

Activity:	Factor chosen:
Explanation:	

Activity:	Factor chosen:
Explanation:	

Activities – different roles

Key point   ✔ There are other types of roles as well as 'performer'.
- These include **helper**, **team-mate**, **opponent** and **official**.

7. Copy and complete the table below. For four different activities, select a different role for each one and provide a description of what is involved in each different role. Some parts of the answer have been included to help you. An example answer is also provided.

Activity	Role	Task description
Tennis	Official	I was a line judge. It was my task to judge whether the ball was 'in' or 'out'.
Badminton	Opponent	
Volleyball	Team-mate	
	Official	
Gymnastics		My partner gave me advice on how to perform my handstand correctly, and then supported me.

8. There are many different roles you carry out when helping a partner in your class. For example, you help by providing advice, by providing opposition in practices and by making sure that they are safe.

Describe two safety factors you have considered while taking part in two different activities. An example answer is provided.

Activity: Swimming	Safety factor: Safe swimming in lanes
Explanation: My group ensured that we swam in one direction only. We then walked back to the start point and repeated this 'lane cycle'. This helped make sure that there were no unnecessary collisions between swimmers in our group.	

Activity 1:	Safety factor:
Explanation:	

Activity 2:	Safety factor:
Explanation:	

9. Officials play important roles in many different activities, for example, the referee in Rugby Union and umpires in Cricket. They require certain personal qualities to help them in their role.

Give two personal qualities required by referees or umpires. Explain why each is important. An example answer is provided.

Activity: Hockey	Role: Umpire	Personal quality: Being fair to both sides
Explanation: The umpires have to treat both teams identically. They need to apply the rules of the game in the same way for both teams.		

Activity:	Role:	Personal quality:
Explanation:		

Activity:	Role:	Personal quality:
Explanation:		

Equipment for activities

Key point ✔ Proper equipment is designed to help your performance and ensure your safety.

10. Choose two different activities. For each, explain how an item of equipment is designed to help you perform safely. An example answer is provided.

Activity: Cross-country running	Equipment: Correct training shoes
Safety reason: Training shoes need to be able to absorb the force of the runner's heel striking the ground on a continuous basis. Training shoes also need to have a good sole grip.	

Activity 1:	Equipment:
Safety reason:	

Activity 2:	Equipment:
Safety reason:	

Rules and codes of conduct

Key points ✔ Rules are designed to shape activities and ensure that everyone can participate on an equal basis.

✔ Codes of conduct (unwritten rules) explain the way in which participation should take place in different activities.

11. Give a safety rule, a rule of fair play and an example of good etiquette, each from a different activity. An example answer is provided.

Activity 1: Trampoline	Safety rule: Must have spotters and mat protection in place.
Activity 2: Hockey	Rule of fair play: Keep stick low to ground when passing.
Activity 3: Football	Code of conduct/etiquette: Return the ball to the other team after an injury stoppage.

Activity 1:	Safety rule:
Activity 2:	Rule of fair play:
Activity 3:	Code of conduct/etiquette:

12. Describe the importance of a safety rule, a rule of fair play and an example of good etiquette, all from the same activity. An example answer is provided.

Activity: Rugby Union
Safety rule: Use of feet in a ruck
Explanation: When opposing players are on the ground, you should be careful not to stamp on them as you try to help your team.
Rule of fair play: Safe play in scrums
Explanation: In a scrum, you must try to keep the scrum 'up' and not try to collapse it.
Code of conduct/etiquette: Shake hands with the other team
Explanation: After the game, you should shake hands as a way of thanking the opposition.

Activity:
Safety rule:
Explanation:
Rule of fair play:
Explanation:
Code of conduct/etiquette:
Explanation:

Scoring systems

Key points
- ✔ There are many different scoring systems for different activities.
- ✔ Some activities have 'objective' scoring based on results.
- ✔ Some activities have 'subjective' scoring based on opinions.
- ✔ Results can be for highest score, lowest times and many other reasons.

13. Copy and complete the following grid.

Activity	Objective/Subjective	How results are decided
Gymnastics	subjective	
Netball		
Cricket	objective	
Table tennis		Number of games won. Each game up to 21 points
Ice dancing		Marks for technical merit and artistic impression
Swimming		

14. Choose one individual activity and one team activity which have objective scoring systems. For each, explain how play is continued in the event of the score being level at the end of the contest/match.

Individual activity:
Explanation:

Team activity:
Explanation:

15. Describe one activity where, in the event of the score ending level (a tie/draw), further participation is not possible and the result has to be decided by other means.

Activity:
Explanation:

16. Choose one activity which uses a subjective scoring system. Describe some of the different criteria which would be used for awarding different marks/points.

Activity:
Explanation:

Tactics and strategies

Key points ✔ Many different tactics and strategies exist for individual and team activities.
✔ Tactics and strategies aim to make the most of your individual/team strengths.
✔ Decisions about your tactics and strategies are made before, during and after performance.

---

17. Outline one benefit of using a tactic in a game.

---

18. Choose one team activity. Name one role you had in that activity. Describe a defensive responsibility and an attacking responsibility that went with this role. An example answer is provided.

Activity: Basketball	Role: Guard
Defensive responsibility: I had to make sure I kept my 'opposite number' away from our basket. The closer she came, the more pressure I put her under.	
Attacking responsibility: I had to help set up our attacking plays by passing to different players. I also took some 'outside' shots if I wasn't being marked and other options were not available.	

Activity:	Role:
Defensive responsibility:	
Attacking responsibility:	

---

19. Choose a tactic from a team activity. Explain how the tactic chosen was well suited for both your individual and team strengths. An example answer is provided.

Activity: Badminton (doubles)	Tactic: Playing 'sides' when defending
Description: When defending, I have good court movement. This helps me move forward and back to play different shots. In addition, my partner is of similar ability to me. As a result, we do not have a weak side which our opponents can exploit by hitting to it when the chance arises.	

Activity:	Tactic:
Description:	

Being creative in activities

✔ In most activities, you devise and create solutions to different problems.
✔ Different activities have different ways of being creative.
✔ Some activities have definite targets, e.g. to score more goals; others have more open-ended aims, e.g. to improve certain qualities in performance.

20. Choose one activity with an objective scoring system. Describe how you worked creatively with team-mates to try to win. An example answer is provided.

> Activity: Volleyball
>
> Explanation: Our opponents were finding it straightforward to predict from where our spike attacks were coming. We decided that we could add more variety to our play by asking our setter to vary the set to unsettle the other team.

> Activity:
>
> Explanation:

21. Choose one activity with a subjective scoring system. Describe how you worked creatively to improve the overall quality of your performance. An example answer is provided.

> Activity: Gymnastics (floor routine)
>
> Explanation: In my floor routine, I had three different cartwheels. To begin with, they were all at the same speed, leading with my left hand on each one. I decided I could add to the quality of my routine by varying the cartwheels. For a start, I performed one of them leading with the right hand. Then I varied the speed — I made one quite slow, one quite quick from a standing start and one quite quick from a run-up.

> Activity:
>
> Explanation:

Size and shape

Key point ✔ Different body size and shape can occasionally help your performance.

22. Complete the following sentences, using the words in bold below. Use each word only once.

thin   tall   muscular   strong   stocky   short

In Rugby, it helps if your front row forwards are relatively _____ and _____.

In High Jump, it helps if you are _____ and _____.

For many sports, it helps if you are quite _____ and _____.

Adapting activities

Key point ✔ Activities can be adapted in many ways. For example, changes can be made to the playing area, the equipment, the rules, the scoring system and the time the activity lasts.

23. Give two advantages of playing 'small side' team games as opposed to 'full side' team games.

Advantage 1:	
Advantage 2:	

24. Describe two advantages of having more attackers than defenders ('numerical superiority') when practising your attacking skills in a team activity.

Advantage 1:	
Advantage 2:	

25. Choose one activity. Explain four ways you could adapt it. An example answer from volleyball is provided.

Activity: Volleyball		
Full activity	*Key Area*	*Adapted activity*
6 v 6	Number of players	4 v 4
Full height	Net height	Lowered to help players
Maximum 3 touches per team	Number of touches	Team allowed more than 3 touches
Ball must not touch ground	Rule change	Ball allowed to touch ground once each possession

Activity:		
Full activity	*Key Area*	*Adapted activity*
	Number of players	
	Rule change	

2. The Body in Action

Fitness overview

Key points ✔ Different activities have different fitness needs.
  ✔ Training has to be specific to your level of ability, fitness and type of activity.
  ✔ Training has to become more demanding in order to be effective.

26. Complete the following sentences about when different fitness factors would be required. Use the words in bold below. Use each word only once.

cardiorespiratory endurance   **muscular endurance**   **speed**
strength   **power**   **flexibility**

To make stretching movements for defending in volleyball, I needed _____.
To be able to throw the javelin far, I needed _____.
To rebound continuously during the whole game, I needed _____ _____.
To make short fast runs into the penalty area, I needed _____.
To keep going for the full 90 minutes, I needed _____ _____.
To hold a handstand, I needed _____.

27. Complete the following sentences about why different players in a hockey team require different types of fitness. Use the words in bold below. Use each word only once.

cardiorespiratory endurance   **muscular endurance**   **speed**
strength   **power**   **flexibility**

The midfield players in our team needed _____ _____ as they had to do so much running in the game. In defence, the defenders needed _____ to cover for each other against attacking players. In attack, our attackers needed _____ to keep possession of the ball when under pressure from defenders challenging them. They also needed _____ when shooting. The goalkeeper needed _____ when diving to save shots. All players needed some _____ _____ in their arm and leg muscles.

28. Choose **two** of the following exercises that are often included in general circuit training.

   shuttle run   squat thrusts   press-ups   bench jumps

For each exercise, explain how you could make the exercise progressively more demanding.

Name of exercise 1:
Explanation:

Name of exercise 2:
Explanation:

---

29. (i) Outline two benefits of assessing your level of fitness at the beginning of a fitness training programme.
    (ii) As your fitness training programme continues, 'overload' is needed. How would you add overload to your programme?

30. Complete the grid for both an individual activity and a team activity of your choice. An example answer is provided.

	Activity	Aspect of fitness	Method of training	Fitness test
Individual activity	Gymnastics	Flexibility	Active stretching	Sit-and-reach test
Individual activity				
Team activity				

For each activity, explain why the **method of training** is effective for the activity and aspect of fitness chosen.

For each activity, explain why the **fitness test** is effective for the activity and aspect of fitness chosen.

31. Choose one exercise or practice drill that you have used in an activity in your course. Firstly, explain why the exercise or practice drill is specific to the chosen activity. Secondly, explain how you could make the exercise or practice drill progressively more demanding. An example answer is provided.

Activity: Basketball	Exercise/Practice drill: Speed dribble in Basketball
Explanation 1: This practice drill is useful to me because it involves me dribbling at the same time as sprinting. I play as a guard; sprinting quickly whilst dribbling is important in this role.	
Explanation 2: I would add to the difficulty by making the sprint times quicker or by reducing my rest times between the speed dribbles.	

Activity:	Exercise/Practice drill:
Explanation 1:	
Explanation 2:	

The skeletal and muscular systems

Key point ✔ Bones, tendons and muscles work together to allow movement to take place.

32.

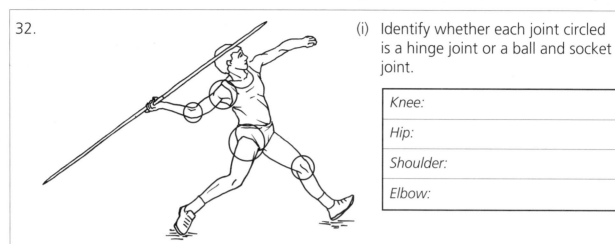

(i) Identify whether each joint circled is a hinge joint or a ball and socket joint.

Knee:	
Hip:	
Shoulder:	
Elbow:	

(ii) Explain the difference between a hinge joint and a ball and socket joint.

---

33. Study the picture of the high jumper.

Explain how the jumper's leg muscles work to help her gain height when jumping.

---

34. Study the picture of the runner. Explain how the muscles, tendons and bones of the main joint used (the knee joint) work together to produce efficient movement.

Joint used: Knee joint (Hinge)	
Explanation:	

See pages 20 and 21 of Leckie & Leckie's *Standard Grade Physical Education Course Notes*   © Leckie & Leckie

The cardiorespiratory system

Key point   ✔ Regular training improves the efficiency of the heart and lungs.

35. Complete the following sentences about the benefits of an efficient cardiorespiratory system. Use the words in bold below. Use each word only once.

oxygen	heart	blood	lungs

Your muscles need energy which is supplied by food and _____. As you breathe in, air enters your _____. There, it is absorbed into your _____ and pumped round your body by your _____.

36. Describe two benefits of regular endurance training for your cardiorespiratory system.

Benefit 1:
Benefit 2:

37. Explain what is meant by the term 'oxygen debt'.

Endurance

Key points   ✔ There are two types of endurance: cardiorespiratory and muscular.
   ✔ Cardiorespiratory endurance is when the greatest physical demand is on the heart and lungs.
   ✔ Muscular endurance is when the greatest physical demand is on a particular set of muscles.
   ✔ Training programmes need to be well planned to bring about improvements.

38. Choose one activity which requires cardiorespiratory endurance. Describe two benefits of cardiorespiratory endurance on your participation in this activity. An example answer is provided.

Activity: Orienteering
Benefits: The courses for my age and ability last about 60 minutes. Good cardiorespiratory endurance ensures that I can keep running for the whole hour and at a quite fast pace.

Activity:
Benefits:

39. (i) Explain three considerations which you would take into account to ensure that any cardiorespiratory training you did was beneficial to aerobic endurance rather than anaerobic endurance.

   (ii) Explain how you would measure your fitness to ensure your training was effective for developing cardiorespiratory endurance.

40. Read the four statements below about **muscular endurance** and select the two which are correct.
   - Cyclists need muscular endurance to keep their leg muscles working for a long time.
   - Hockey players need muscular endurance to help them shoot.
   - When kayaking, my arm muscles need muscular endurance when going upstream.
   - On the trampoline, you need muscular endurance to complete a 5-bounce sequence.

41. (i) The most common type of training to improve muscular endurance is circuit training. Write down the major muscle groups which are being exercised at each of the following circuit training exercises.

Sit-ups   Burpees   Press-ups

Dips   Shuttle run   Step-ups

Sit-ups:	*Dips:*
Burpees:	*Shuttle run:*
Press-ups:	*Step-ups:*

(ii) Choose three of the six exercises. Describe how you could make each exercise increasingly demanding over a number of weeks.

Exercise 1:
Explanation:

Exercise 2:
Explanation:

Exercise 3:
Explanation:

Answers to Leckie & Leckie's
Questions in Standard Grade Physical Education

Answers to Foundation level questions are printed on a plain background (like this).

Answers to General level questions are printed on a hatched background (like this).

Answers to Credit level questions are printed on a shaded background (like this).

These specimen answers provide examples of responses at the different levels. Many questions could have answers attempted at a level above the one indicated. For example, many General level questions could be answered at Credit level provided the answer shows greater depth in its description and explanation.

Answers to 1. Activities

Types of activity

1.

Activity	Individual Activity	Team/Group Activity
Basketball		✔
Social dancing		✔
Marathon running	✔	
4 x 400 m relay		✔
Badminton	✔	✔
800 m	✔	

2. (i) Competitive activity involves some form of contest between different individuals or teams. Winning is a major aim of the activity.
   (ii) Non-competitive means taking part for reasons other than winning. These could be social reasons, for fitness or for sense of achievement.

3.

'I enjoy getting out and meeting other people. We all take part together and then go out afterwards.'	Social
'I like the challenge. I need the thrill of competing against myself when I am rock climbing.'	Personal
'Regular exercise is good for me. It is not too difficult, but demanding enough to help me to live a long and healthy life.'	Health
'Swimming is my favourite sport. The longer events are great for my endurance and the sprint events are great for improving power.'	Physical

4. Each answer should provide a correct identification of type of activity linked to a logical well-described explanation of why you value participation in each of the activities.

5. Example answer:

Younger age activity: Gymnastics	Explanation: You are most likely to participate in Gymnastics at a young age only. Gymnastics requires considerable flexibility and a very good power-to-weight ratio. You are most likely to have these physical qualities at a young age.
Lifelong activity: Golf	Explanation: Golf is a skilful game but is not too physically demanding. You can take your time playing. It is therefore a suitable activity for all ages.

6. Example answers:

Activity: Basketball	Factor chosen: Disability
Explanation: Most games halls have wheelchair access. Wheelchair basketball is now a very popular activity. Major events such as The Paralympic Games have helped promote sport for the less able-bodied.	
Activity: Skiing	Factor chosen: Weather
Explanation: The weather can affect your skiing progress. Good weather can help your skiing whilst poor weather can result in limited snow and often poor overhead conditions.	

Activities – different roles

7. Example answer:

Activity	Role	Task description
Badminton	Opponent	I played an attacking game based on using smashes and downward shots whenever I could.
Volleyball	Team-mate	I set as accurately as I could so that my team-mates who were spiking had every chance of winning each rally with their spike.
Basketball	Official	I worked as a timekeeper. When the ball was out of play, I stopped the clock.
Gymnastics	Helper	My partner gave me advice on how to perform my handstand correctly, and then supported me.

8. See example answer provided with question.

9. See example answer provided with question. Other correct answers have to explain the importance of the personal qualities required. Personal qualities include: honesty; fairness; being able to work with others as part of an official team of referees, assistant referees, line judges, timekeepers, etc.

Equipment for activities

10. See example answer provided with question. Other correct answers have to link the item of equipment selected to safe participation in the chosen activity.

Rules and codes of conduct

11. See example answer provided with question.

12. See example answer provided with question.

Scoring systems

13.

Activity	Objective/Subjective	How results are decided
Gymnastics	subjective	Points at different disciplines such as floor, vault and bar(s)
Netball	objective	More points scored than the opposition
Cricket	objective	Runs scored/other team bowled out
Table tennis	objective	Number of games won. Each game up to 21 points
Ice dancing	subjective	Marks for technical merit and artistic impression
Swimming	objective	Time taken decides 1st, 2nd, 3rd, etc

14. Example answers:

Individual activity: Golf

Explanation: Extra holes are played until a winner is found.

Team activity: Football

Explanation: Replays, extra time, 'golden goal' and penalty shoot outs are all used to decide the winner.

15. Example answer:

Activity: Athletics (track)

Explanation: Running events are decided by judges who have to make a decision about who is the winner. Photo finishes are often needed.

16. Example answer:

Activity: Gymnastics (floor)

Explanation: For a floor sequence, the judges need to consider such factors as the difficulty of different moves, the way the mat area is used and how well the sequence links to the music used.

Tactics and strategies

17. It makes the winning of the game easier as you are trying to play to your strengths.

18. See example answer provided with question.

19. See example answer provided with question.

Being creative in activities

20. See example answer provided with question.

21. See example answer provided with question.

Size and shape

22. In Rugby, it helps if your front row forwards are relatively short and stocky.
In High Jump, it helps if you are tall and thin.
For many sports, it helps if you are quite strong and muscular.

Adapting activities

23. Example answer:

> Advantage 1: Each player has a greater chance to be more involved in the game.
>
> Advantage 2: Each player is able to keep up with the game more as the pitch is smaller.

(Other answers could include those relating to fewer rules, shorter playing time, easier to work with team-mates.)

24. Example answer:

> Advantage 1: The practice is more likely to be successful because of the extra player/players.
>
> Advantage 2: Attackers are under less pressure than usual. This allows confidence in possession to increase.

(Other answers could include the advantages of finding space more easily, of having more opportunities to refine skills and of having more time to carry out specific moves.)

25. See example answer provided with question. Answer must be specific to one identified activity throughout.

Answers to 2. The Body in Action

Fitness overview

26. To make stretching movements for defending in volleyball, I needed flexibility.
    To be able to throw the javelin far, I needed power.
    To rebound continuously during the whole game, I needed muscular endurance.
    To make short fast runs into the penalty area, I needed speed.
    To keep going for the full 90 minutes, I needed cardiorespiratory endurance.
    To hold a handstand, I needed strength.

27. The midfield players in our team needed cardiorespiratory endurance as they had to do so much running in the game. In defence, the defenders needed speed to cover for each other against attacking players. In attack, our attackers needed strength to keep possession of the ball when under pressure from defenders challenging them. They also needed power when shooting. The goalkeeper needed flexibility when diving to save shots. All players needed some muscular endurance in their arm and leg muscles.

28. Each explanation should refer to applying the principle of progressive overload by making the exercise more demanding (intensity), carried out for longer (duration) or carried out more often (frequency).

29. (i) It allows you to set an appropriate workload. It is also easy to measure improvements to your fitness.
    (ii) Overload can be added in three ways. Each exercise can be made more difficult (intensity), each exercise can be performed more often (frequency) and each exercise can be performed for longer (duration).

30. **method of training** The answers for both the individual activity and the team activity chosen need to show a relevant and correctly explained relationship between the activity, aspect of fitness and method of training chosen.
    fitness test The answers for both the individual activity and the team activity chosen need to show a relevant and correctly explained relationship between the activity, aspect of fitness and fitness test chosen.

31. See example answer provided with question.

The skeletal and muscular systems

32. (i)

Knee: Hinge
Hip: Ball and socket
Shoulder: Ball and socket
Elbow: Hinge

    (ii) A hinge joint can move in one plane only (opening and closing like a door) whereas a ball and socket joint can move in all planes.

33. As one set of leg muscles contracts (the agonist), the opposite set of muscles extends (the antagonist). In this example, the high jumper's front thigh muscles contract (whilst the back thigh muscles become extended) to straighten the take-off leg and power the jump.

34.

Joint used: Knee joint (Hinge)

Explanation: The knee joint allows the upper and lower leg bones to move relative to each other (i.e. the knee bends). The tendons join muscles to bones. As the muscles contract (shorten in length), they pull on the tendons which pull on the bones to produce movement. Then the opposing muscles contract and pull on their tendons to move the bones in the other direction.

The cardiorespiratory system

35. Your muscles need energy which is supplied by food and *oxygen*. As you breathe in, air enters your *lungs*. There, it is absorbed into your *blood* and pumped round your body by your *heart*.

36.

Benefit 1: The heart becomes bigger and more efficient. More blood can be pushed to the muscles per heart beat (stroke volume).

Benefit 2: More air can be breathed in by the lungs (increased vital capacity). This gives the body more oxygen in each breath.

37. As you exercise, it takes a short time for your heart rate to increase. During this time, your need for oxygen is greater than your supply. You work anaerobically for a while – hence the term 'oxygen debt'.

Endurance

38. See example answer provided with question.

39. (i)
- I would need to calculate my training zone.
- I would carry out specific training that would raise my pulse rate into my training zone. (Long continuous running would be one option.)
- I would ensure that my pulse stayed within my training zone for between 20–30 minutes for my training to be effective.

(ii) I would regularly check my pulse to ensure my heart rate was within my training zone.

40.
- Cyclists need muscular endurance to keep their leg muscles working for a long time. **correct**
- Hockey players need muscular endurance to help them shoot. **false**
- When kayaking, my arm muscles need muscular endurance when going upstream. **correct**
- On the trampoline, you need muscular endurance to complete a 5-bounce sequence. **false**

Sit-ups: Abdominals	Dips: Arms and shoulders
Burpees: Legs, abdominals and shoulders	Shuttle run: Legs and shoulders
Press-ups: Arms and shoulders	Step-ups: Legs

(ii) Example answers:

Exercise 1: Press-ups

Explanation: I could do more of them in the same time.

Exercise 2: Dips

Explanation: I could pause when my arms are low to the bar each time and hold this position for a few seconds.

Exercise 3: Step-ups

Explanation: I could do the exercise for longer: 40 seconds instead of 30 seconds.

42.

Reason 1: To provide you with information about your fitness progress at each exercise station.

Reason 2: The information collected would allow you to make decisions about overloading at each station.

Strength fitness

43.
- Swimmers need strength to keep swimming for a long time. **false**
- You need strength in your arms and shoulders to hold a handstand for a few seconds. **correct**
- Rugby players need strength to be able to tackle. **correct**
- You need strength to putt well in golf. **false**

44. For a strength training programme, you need to exercise specific *muscle* groups. You need to ensure that the *workload* of each exercise is high with *low* repetitions. As the training programme progresses, you need to add *overload* to the programme.

45. You would alter the weight used. You would use a different combination of workload to repetition. Muscular endurance would require a high number of repetitions with a low workload, approximately 50% of maximum capacity. Strength would require less repetitions but with a higher workload, approximately 80% of maximum capacity.

46. Isometric training exercises are useful for activities where you may need to hold the muscles tense and still (for example, during handstands and other inverted balances in gymnastics where you have to take your whole weight on your arms).
Isotonic training exercises are useful for activities where you may need to move the working muscles (for example, in butterfly and other swimming strokes, where a regular cycle of the arms is required to move your arms through the water).

Power

47.	• Swimmers need power for their racing dive at the start of the race. **correct** • You need power to dig the ball successfully in volleyball. **false** • Hockey goalkeepers need power to help them stop fast shots. **false** • You need power to throw the discus effectively. **correct**
48.	See example answers provided with question.
49.	Example answer:

Activity: Tennis	Skill: Service Reception
Explanation: The performer has to react quickly to the speed and angle of the serve. Often the chosen return of serve will involve quick court movement to play a powerful return.	

Speed

50.	See example answers provided with question.

Flexibility

51.	See example answers provided with question.

Preparing for action

52.	A warm up is an important part of your preparation for activity. It should begin with some gentle jogging to raise your pulse. After this, you should do some stretching exercises that will help your flexibility. You may then want to practise some of the skills involved in the activity.
53.	(i) To raise the pulse and increase blood flow to the muscles. (ii) To allow muscles to move more easily and to improve the flexibility in joints. (iii) It reduces stiffness in muscles and helps return the body to a resting state.
54.	See example answer provided with question. Your answer should include details of two specific exercises you used.

Answers to 3. Skills and Techniques

Easy skills and complex skills

55.	When learning to perform a new skill or technique, you try to make it as easy as possible. You can do this by making the movements flow together in a simple order. As you become better, you can make the skill or technique more complex. You can make your skill or technique practice more difficult in many ways, for example, by practising for longer. This may make it more tiring for you.
56.	See example answer provided with question.
57.	See example answer provided with question.
58.	See example answers provided with question.

Breaking down a skill

59. The correct order is: (1) run-up   (2) take-off   (3) first flight   (4) second flight   (5) landing.

60. See example answer provided with question.

61.

Activity	Gymnastics	Badminton	Basketball
Skill/Technique	Forward Roll	High Serve	Jump Shot
Preparation 1	Feet together	Stand 'side on'	Feet together
Preparation 2	Head tucked in	Take racket back	Look at target
Action 1	Take weight on hands	Transfer weight forward	Controlled jump
Action 2	Keep legs together	Smooth racket swing	Release at full height
Recovery 1	Open out carefully	High follow-through	Land in balance
Recovery 2	Finish standing still	Be ready for next shot	React to shot result

62. See example answer provided with question.

Learning skills

63.

Activity: Swimming	Technique: Back crawl	
Push off from the side, gentle continuous leg kick, take six arm strokes, then stand.		3
Push off from the side, hold one float under each arm, leg kick for one width.		1
Push off from the side, swim continuously for one 20 m length of back crawl, full stroke.		4
Push off from the side, hold one float across chest, leg kick for one length of the pool.		2

64. Example answers:

> Reason 1: You have more time to practise different skills and techniques you have learned.
>
> Reason 2: You have more confidence to try different moves.
>
> Reason 3: You can practise when under less pressure as there are fewer defenders.

65. Sometimes it is difficult to break down continuous actions such as a gymnastics vault into whole-part-whole sections. It is easier to practise such a skill by building the skill up progressively, adding to the difficulty of the vault bit by bit.

66. See example answer provided with question.

Feedback

67.
- Receiving feedback immediately after your performance is best. **true**
- Negative feedback about what you are doing wrong will help you learn. **false**
- Knowledge of results is a useful form of external feedback. **true**
- Detailed feedback on at least 10 different points is needed to learn simple skills. **false**
- Positive feedback on a few key points works well. **true**
- You receive internal feedback during your performance. **true**

68. Answers could include the following points:
    - Feedback should be positive, clear and precise.
    - He should give feedback as soon as possible after performance.
    - He should focus on a few key points that will help the performer.

69. Internal feedback is the feedback you 'feel' yourself during your performance. For example, when swimming, you can 'feel' whether your hand is in the right 'catch' position before the pull begins. External feedback either comes from other people (for example, your coach discusses the qualities in your performance) or from the results of your performance, both during and after activity (for example, race times).

70. See example answer provided with question.

Practising skills

71. (i) You can become familiar with the movements involved in a skill or technique. The movements can become automatic.
    (ii) You might become tired. You can become bored by repeating the same practice.

72. • Make the defender play 'active' rather than 'passive' defence.
    • Make it 3 v 1 instead of 4 v 1 – this will make the three players work harder.
    • Make the four attackers play 'two-touch' then, later, 'one-touch' only. This will make ball control and possession more difficult to achieve.

73. • You can concentrate more on other parts of the game. For example, in Basketball, being able to dribble correctly means that you can look up and see who is open to receive a pass.
    • You can move more easily whilst still paying attention to other things. For example, in Badminton, you can move backwards and get into a side on position to play an overhead clear shot. Avoiding looking down makes it easier to keep looking at the shuttlecock.

74. (i) See example answer provided with question.
    (ii) See example answer provided with question.

Centre of gravity

75. The gymnast performing the headstand has a static centre of gravity as she is trying to hold her balance above her base of support (which is created by her arms and head). The skier has a dynamic (constantly moving) centre of gravity as she is moving when skiing. In this example, the skier's centre of gravity is affected by the turning of the skis and the terrain.

76. See example answer provided with question.

77. See example answers provided with question.

Transferring your weight

78. A swimmer uses *force* to overcome *resistance*. A Rugby Union player taking a penalty kick from a long *distance* has a long follow-through in her kick. This helps add *power* to the kick. A long distance runner keeps his centre of *gravity* at the same *height* as he runs forward.

79. See example answer provided with question.

80. See example answer provided with question.

Force, friction and leverage

81.	See example answer provided with question.

82.	(i) See example answer provided with question.
	(ii) See example answer provided with question.

83.	See example answers provided with question.

Answers to 4. Evaluating Performance

84. (i) Gymnastics – forward roll

Body:	Faces forward, reaches out with arms, rolls over and regains standing position.
Order:	First hands, then upper to lower back roll on the ground before regaining standing position.
Shape:	Slightly open tuck, knees flexed and drawn in towards chest. Rounded back. Legs together.
Speed:	Controlled medium speed, drive from knees controlling speed of roll.

(ii) Basketball – left-hand lay-up

Body:	Faces towards basket. Aims to run to lay ball up onto backboard.
Order:	Runs towards basket, takes off right foot, lands both feet together at the same time.
Shape:	Drives towards basket in normal running shape then jumps as high as possible off one foot.
Speed:	Moves in at a steady, controlled speed which is as fast as possible without technique breaking down.

(iii) Tennis – backhand

Body:	Moves into 'side on' position. Racket is held in right hand. Eyes on ball throughout.
Order:	Run towards the ball, take the racket back early, transfer weight from back to front foot, follow through.
Shape:	Upper body turns away from approaching ball, legs bent, shoulders unwind when striking ball.
Speed:	Move into position as early as possible. The striking action is usually fast and powerful.

(iv) Gymnastics – handspring

Body:	Runs forward, reaches out with extended arms, legs keep extended as they overtake arms to resume standing position.
Order:	Runs up, both hands strike mat together, legs land together.
Shape:	Extended position in run-up approach, legs bend to begin drive, arms together and extended.
Speed:	Accelerating run-up, fast strong leg swing to generate rotation.

(v) Gymnastics – neck spring

Body:	Two-footed take-off, reaches out with arms, shoulders lowered to box top, arms drive to extended position to create flight off box top.
Order:	Two-footed take-off, arms make contact with box top together, legs land together.
Shape:	Extended start and flight onto box top. Arms bend to allow open rounded shape before drive to produce open arched extended position.
Speed:	Moderate speed run-up, controlled flight onto box top, strong drive to finishing position.

5. Examination Preparation

You will want to ensure that your Course revision is rewarded by completing your video exam successfully. The following advice should help you to achieve your goal.

✔ Each question is in four parts. Parts (a) and (b) are on Evaluating. Parts (c) and (d) are on Knowledge and Understanding. Time is available during the examination for you to review your answers.

✔ Watch the video closely. The commentary will indicate how many times you will see the action. **Listen carefully** to the commentary. Make sure you watch **each viewing** closely. Ensure that you view when you should. Avoid writing when you should be watching. Sufficient time is available for completing your written answer after you have viewed the different actions.

✔ Parts (a) and (b) of every question ask you to **observe and describe** what different performers are doing and to **suggest improvements**. You need to be careful to avoid answering about what performers are not doing. Negative answers about what performers are doing wrong are not acceptable. Describe accurately what performers are doing and, if required, suggest improvements they could make to their action.

✔ Answer in as much detail as you can. Some answers may be for 3 marks. For these questions, you will need to provide some detailed observations and judgements in your answer. Make it clear what it is you are writing about. For example, if you are suggesting improvements to a Gymnastics sequence which involves different balances, ensure that your answer correctly mentions Balance 1, Balance 2 or Balance 3 as requiring improvement. In this way, your answer contains more specific detail. An answer such as 'keep legs straight' is more likely to gain marks if you can complete it with 'keep legs straight in the second balance'.

✔ Select activities which are common in schools as part of your answer. Do not answer by writing about Snooker, Pool, Darts or any form of motor sport. If 'stuck', consider first the activities which are part of your Standard Grade course.

✔ Finally, study the example on the next page.

Answers page 11

✔ Try to avoid being upset by the 'activity focus'. Many different activities are taught in Standard Grade courses – you will probably see questions which use activities which are not part of your course. However, the questions are all general in nature rather than activity-specific.

For example, a question may use Rugby as the activity focus. You may be asked about how well the defenders control the attackers' space. This is the type of detail you will have covered in your course, perhaps not in Rugby but in another activity, for example Basketball. Therefore, try to relate your knowledge and understanding from your experience in one activity to another.

Activity focus – Rugby

Question – How could the defender try to gain possession of the ball?

Activity focus – Basketball

Answer – Move towards attacker with ball

Answers page 12

42. Circuit training programmes to improve muscular endurance often last many weeks. Give two reasons why regularly re-testing your progress at each exercise station would be useful during your programme.

Reason 1:	
Reason 2:	

Strength fitness

Key point ✔ Strength training programmes need to be well planned; increases in weight should be gradual.

43. Read the four statements below about **strength** and select the two which are correct.
    - Swimmers need strength to keep swimming for a long time.
    - You need strength in your arms and shoulders to hold a handstand for a few seconds.
    - Rugby players need strength to be able to tackle.
    - You need strength to putt well in golf.

44. Complete the following sentences using the words in bold below. Use each word only once.

   muscle   workload   overload   low

   For a strength training programme, you need to exercise specific _____ groups. You need to ensure that the _____ of each exercise is high with _____ repetitions. As the training programme progresses, you need to add _____ to the programme.

45. Explain how you could use the same weight machine or free-standing weight exercise for both muscular endurance and strength.

46. These two performers need different types of strength. The gymnast performing a handstand needs **static strength**. For the swimmer, **dynamic strength** is important.

   Explain why the gymnast would benefit from **isometric exercises** and why the swimmer would benefit from **isotonic exercises**.

Power

Key point ✔ Power is strength and speed used together in a single action.

47. Read the four statements below about **power** and select the two which are correct.
    - Swimmers need power for their racing dive at the start of the race.
    - You need power to dig the ball successfully in volleyball.
    - Hockey goalkeepers need power to help them stop fast shots.
    - You need power to throw the discus effectively.

48. Choose one individual activity and one team activity. In each, explain how **power** is required in one skill. Example answers are provided.

Individual activity: Athletics	Skill: Throwing (javelin)
Explanation: To throw the javelin far, you need power. You need to be quite physically strong and have speed in your throwing arm to bring it forward quickly. Linking speed and strength together can produce a powerful throw.	

Team activity: Volleyball	Skill: Spiking
Explanation: To spike effectively in volleyball, you often have to prepare by moving quickly into position to make a strong powerful jump. As you jump, you take your arm back, ready for a powerful downward spike.	

Individual activity:	Skill:
Explanation:	

Team activity:	Skill:
Explanation:	

49. Power is linked to explosive actions that require speed, strength and also split-second timing, for example, a sprint start. Here, the athlete needs sprinting speed as well as a very short reaction time to the starting signal.

Choose one skill in one activity where a combination of **power** and **reaction time** is required. Explain your choice fully.

Activity:	Skill:
Explanation:	

Speed

Key point   ✔ Having speed means being able to cover a distance or perform different movements in a short time.

50. Choose one individual activity and one team activity. In each, explain how **speed** is required in one skill. Example answers are provided.

Individual activity: Gymnastics	Skill: Flight (vaulting)
Explanation: The run-up approach requires speed. You need to accelerate quickly over a few steps. You need a fast take-off to help gain flight.	

Team activity: Football	Skill: Dribbling
Explanation: As a winger, I often need speed to pass a defender when dribbling. I knock the ball past him and then sprint after it to regain control.	

Individual activity:	Skill:
Explanation:	

Team activity:	Skill:
Explanation:	

Flexibility

Key point   ✔ Flexibility is the range of movement in a joint.

51. Choose one individual activity and one team activity. In each, explain how **flexibility** is required in one skill. Example answers are provided.

Individual activity: Athletics	Skill: Hurdling
Explanation: I needed a big range of movement in my hips to help my performance. I needed a long straight lead leg and a short 'tucked-in' trailing leg. Stretching exercises improved my flexibility for hurdling and allowed me to achieve a good shape when crossing the hurdles.	

Team activity: Dance	Skill: Flight
Explanation: In my dance performance, four of us had to move across the stage doing split leaps in the air at one point. These required flexibility in order to achieve the correct shape in the air with legs straight — one leg out in front and one leg behind — and with arms used for balance.	

Individual activity:	Skill:
Explanation:	

Team activity:	Skill:
Explanation:	

Preparing for action

Key point ✔ Effective preparation can enhance the quality of your performance.

---

52. Complete the following sentences using the words in bold below. Use each word only once.

    pulse   **stretching**   **skills**   **jogging**   **preparation**

    A warm up is an important part of your _____ for activity. It should begin with some gentle _____ to raise your _____. After this, you should do some _____ exercises that will help your flexibility. You may then want to practise some of the _____ involved in the activity.

---

53. Warming up before activity and warming down after activity are good ideas.

    (i)   Why is light jogging carried out at the beginning of a warm up?

    (ii) Why is it followed by stretching?

    (iii) Why is a warm down carried out at the end of an activity?

    Give two reasons in each answer.

---

54. Choose one activity. Explain how you would organise your warm up for this activity. Your answer should include details of two specific exercises you used. An example answer is provided.

    Activity: Badminton

    Explanation: My warm up consisted of gentle jogging and stretching exercises. I tried to keep both specific to Badminton. For my jogging, I moved at a gentle pace around the Badminton court – this involved changing direction. For my stretching exercises, I concentrated on the shoulders and trunk. One exercise was called 'trunk twists' and involved turning and twisting from 'face on' to 'side on'. Another was called 'side leans' – this involved using one hand to pull the opposite arm over my head whilst leaning to the side. I completed each exercise six times as part of my overall stretching.

    Activity:

    Explanation:

---

3. Skills and Techniques

Easy skills and complex skills

Key points ✔ A skill is the purpose of a movement.
✔ A technique is a way of performing a skill.
✔ Many different factors make skills range from easy to complex.

---

55. Complete the following sentences using the words in bold below. Use each word only once.

    difficult　　　　**easy**　　　　**complex**　　　　**tiring**　　　　**movements**

    When learning to perform a new skill or technique, you try to make it as _____ as possible. You can do this by making the _____ flow together in a simple order. As you become better, you can make the skill or technique more _____. You can make your skill or technique practice more _____ in many ways, for example, by practising for longer. This may make it more _____ for you.

---

56. Choose two **individual** activities. For each, describe one way in which the skill or technique practice was made more demanding. An example answer is provided.

Activity: Gymnastics — handstand
Explanation: In the first practice, my partner stood in front of me and supported me with both arms. In the second practice, my partner stood beside me and supported me with one arm only.

Activity 1:
Explanation:

Activity 2:
Explanation:

---

57. Choose two **team** activities. For each, describe one way in which the skill or technique practice was made more demanding. An example answer is provided.

Activity: Volleyball
Explanation: In a dig practice, the speed of the 'feed' was increased. This meant I had less time to react to the ball coming towards me.

Activity 1:
Explanation:

Activity 2:
Explanation:

58. Choose one individual and one team activity. For the individual activity, explain the importance of co-ordination in the chosen skill or technique. For the team activity, explain the importance of decision-making in the chosen skill or technique. Example answers are provided.

Importance of Co-ordination	
Individual Activity: Swimming	Skill/Technique: Breast stroke
Explanation: In this stroke, it is important to establish a pull-breathe-kick action that is co-ordinated and fluent. This helps the timing involved in the stroke and helps your leg and arm action to be effective.	

Importance of Decision-making	
Team Activity: Rugby	Skill/Technique: Passing
Explanation: When passing, I had very little time to decide when and to whom to pass. Making decisions quickly is needed for skilful players.	

Importance of Co-ordination	
Individual Activity:	Skill/Technique:
Explanation:	

Importance of Decision-making	
Team Activity:	Skill/Technique:
Explanation:	

Breaking down a skill

Key point ✔ Preparation/Action/Recovery is an effective way of analysing a skill or technique.

59. For a vault in Gymnastics, arrange the following words in the correct order in terms of Preparation/Action/Recovery.

    second flight   take-off   landing   first flight   run-up

60. Choose one directly competitive activity. Explain the importance of **playing area**, **level of opposition** and **number of opponents** in helping you to break down the skills of the activity chosen. You should use a different skill for each part of your answer. An example answer for 'playing area' is provided.

Activity: Hockey	
Importance of Playing Area	
Skill: Passing	Explanation: The playing area was made bigger in order to make the skill easier to learn. We had more time to break the skill down — we controlled the ball, looked around, and then passed accurately as we had more space around us.

Activity:	
Importance of Playing Area	
Skill:	Explanation:
Importance of Level of Opposition	
Skill:	Explanation:
Importance of Number of Opponents	
Skill:	Explanation:

61. Complete the following table, giving two examples of Preparation, Action and Recovery for each skill/technique shown.

Activity	Gymnastics	Badminton	Basketball
Skill/Technique	Forward Roll	High Serve	Jump Shot
Preparation 1			
Preparation 2			
Action 1			
Action 2			
Recovery 1			
Recovery 2			

62. Choose one activity. Explain how you could organise practices for the Preparation, Action or Recovery part of a chosen skill or technique. An example answer is provided.

Activity: Squash	Skill/Technique: Forehand return of serve
Explanation: I isolated the Preparation part of this technique. I completed movement practices that involved me moving quickly from the 'T' to the corner. When doing this, I had to concentrate on moving and turning my shoulders so that my racket would be correctly aligned for the Action part of my forehand return of serve.	

Activity:	Skill/Technique:
Explanation:	

Learning skills

Key points ✔ The whole-part-whole method is an effective way to learn complex skills.
✔ Another effective way to learn skills is by progression, 'bit by bit'.

63. Number this list of practices from '1' to '4' in order of difficulty, using '1' for the easiest and '4' for the most difficult practice.

Activity: Swimming	Technique: Back crawl	
Push off from the side, gentle continuous leg kick, take six arm strokes, then stand.		
Push off from the side, hold one float under each arm, leg kick for one width.		
Push off from the side, swim continuously for one 20 m length of back crawl, full stroke.		
Push off from the side, hold one float across chest, leg kick for one length of the pool.		

64. Give three reasons why, when playing attackers versus defenders in any team game, learning skills for attacking can often be made easier by having more attackers than defenders.

Reason 1:
Reason 2:
Reason 3:

65. Explain why progression may be a better practice method than the whole-part-whole method for continuous skills or techniques.

66. Choose a skill or technique from both an individual activity and a team activity. Explain how you organise your practices for either the Preparation, the Action or the Recovery part of the skill or technique. An example answer is provided.

Team Activity: Basketball	Skill/Technique: Shooting (right-hand lay-up)	P/A/R Area: Action

Explanation: I was driving to the basket well but not scoring enough. I decided to slow down and work on the Action part of the technique. I took a step then a jump off my left foot. I took my right arm up high and concentrated on laying the ball softly onto the 'magic spot' of the backboard. The high jump and soft release of the ball helped me score more baskets in practice and then in full games.

Individual Activity:	Skill/Technique:	P/A/R Area:
Explanation:		

Team Activity:	Skill/Technique:	P/A/R Area:
Explanation:		

Feedback

Key point ✔ Feedback is information you receive about your performance.

67. Answer true or false to the following statements on feedback and its importance in your learning:

- Receiving feedback immediately after your performance is best.
- Negative feedback about what you are doing wrong will help you learn.
- Knowledge of results is a useful form of external feedback.
- Detailed feedback on at least 10 different points is needed to learn simple skills.
- Positive feedback on a few key points works well.
- You receive internal feedback during your performance.

68. This coach is giving feedback. Describe three important points the coach should consider before offering feedback.

69. Explain the difference between internal and external feedback.

70. Choose one activity from your Standard Grade course. Explain how one type of internal feedback and one type of external feedback played a part in your performance development. An example answer is provided.

Activity: Orienteering	
Internal Feedback: Pace judgement	External Feedback: Reading map carefully
Explanation: When I was running, I could usually tell that I was moving at the right pace by using my personal experience of similar Orienteering courses. My past experience let me know how I should feel after a few miles of running in difficult terrain. At the same time, I gained external feedback from being able to read the map carefully. I was able to judge the correct speed to run based on the length of the course and the type of terrain over which I would be moving between the different control points.	

Activity:
Internal Feedback:
Explanation:
External Feedback:
Explanation:

Practising skills

Key point ✔ Practising your skills can make them become automatic in your performance.

71. (i) Give one reason why repeating a practice can help you learn.
    (ii) Give two reasons why practising for too long can be a problem.

72. In this practice, four 'attackers' are trying to keep possession of the ball whilst staying in the box. There is one 'defender' (wearing a dark top) who has been asked to provide passive opposition.
    Explain three ways in which this practice could be made more demanding.

73. Describe two advantages of being able to carry out some skills or techniques automatically in fast-moving continuous team games.

74. (i) Choose one activity in which you have had to **adapt** a skill or technique in order to improve your overall performance. An example answer is provided.

Activity: Volleyball	Skill/Technique: Spiking
Explanation: During a game, many of my diagonal spikes were being retrieved by the opposing team. I adapted the angle of the spike — I began spiking 'down the line'. Having two options made me more successful.	

Activity:	Skill/Technique:
Explanation:	

(ii) Choose one activity in which you have had to **change** a skill or technique in order to improve your overall performance. An example answer is provided.

Activity: Hockey	Skill/Technique: Hitting
Explanation: When playing outdoor hockey, I was doing a type of 'slap hit' — my right hand was halfway down the stick. However, this type of hit was often intercepted as it lacked power. I therefore changed my hand position to both hands at the top of the stick. I was able to gain more power in each hit from a larger swing.	

Activity:	Skill/Technique:
Explanation:	

Centre of gravity

Key points ✔ A low centre of gravity and a large base of support makes you more stable.
  ✔ The position of your centre of gravity is important for maintaining balance.

75. Study the two figures. One has a static centre of gravity and one has a dynamic (constantly moving) centre of gravity. Identify which is which and explain the reasons for your choice.

76. Choose one skill or technique that requires static balance. Explain three practices of increasing difficulty you completed to improve this skill or technique. An example answer is provided.

Skill/Technique: Handstand
Practice 1: I did a handstand against a wall. This provided a lot of support.
Practice 2: I did a handstand with support from my partner. He stood in front of me and provided support with both arms. This provided less support than a wall, but he still had a good hold of me if necessary.
Practice 3: This time my partner stood by my side and provided a single arm support behind my knees. This provided less support than practice 2 — it was more 'up to me' to find my balance. If I lost my balance and began to fall forward, my partner could provide support.

Skill/Technique:
Practice 1:
Practice 2:
Practice 3:

77. Choose two different skills or techniques, one requiring good static balance and one requiring good dynamic balance. How did you manage to remain still and in control of your centre of gravity in the static balance? How did you manage to remain in control of your centre of gravity in the dynamic balance? Example answers are provided.

Skill/Technique requiring static balance: Arabesque in Gymnastics
Explanation: To remain still in this static balance, I had to control all my movements as I moved into and out of the balance and, most importantly, during the balance. I started from a standing position and slowly went into the balance and found the best position to hold. When there, I held the balance as still as possible, making some slight adjustments to the positions of my hands and feet. I came out of the balance in a slow, controlled way.

Skill/Technique requiring dynamic balance: Spiking in Volleyball
Explanation: To remain in control during my spike action, I made sure that I controlled my forward approach to the net. I made sure I jumped up high off two feet. To help me do this, I moved into a balanced jumping position with a quite wide base of support and low centre of gravity. This gave me control when jumping.

Skill/Technique requiring static balance:
Explanation:

Skill/Technique requiring dynamic balance:
Explanation:

Transferring your weight

Key point ✔ Transferring your weight allows different skills and techniques to be performed more effectively.

78. Complete the following sentences using the words in bold below. Use each word only once.

   power   **gravity**   **resistance**   **distance**   **height**   **force**

   A swimmer uses _____ to overcome _____. A Rugby Union player taking a penalty kick from a long _____ has a long follow-through in her kick. This helps add _____ to the kick. A long distance runner keeps his centre of _____ at the same _____ as he runs forward.

79. Many actions in different activities involve a transfer of weight from back foot to front foot. For three different activities, choose one skill or technique which is made more effective by transferring weight in this way. An example answer is provided.

Activity: Badminton	Skill/Technique: High serve
Explanation: As the racket begins its downswing, you begin to transfer your weight forward. This makes it easier to generate the timing and power needed to serve high and deep to the back of the court.	

Activity 1:	Skill/Technique:
Explanation:	

Activity 2:	Skill/Technique:
Explanation:	

Activity 3:	Skill/Technique:
Explanation:	

80. Choose one activity and explain how improving your transfer of weight has improved your performance. An example answer is provided.

Activity: Indoor hockey	Skill/Technique: Push passing
Explanation: I found that by transferring my weight forward from a low angle, placing my left foot close to the ball, I was able to generate more power in my push pass.	

Activity:	Skill/Technique:
Explanation:	

See page 39 of Leckie & Leckie's *Standard Grade Physical Education Course Notes*

© Leckie & Leckie

Force, friction and leverage

Key points ✔ You can use force to overcome friction and resistance in some activities.
              ✔ You use short and long levers as necessary in different actions.

---

81. Choose one activity. Explain how you tried to be streamlined in order to help your performance. An example answer is provided.

> *Activity:* Cycling
>
> *Explanation:* I wore special tight-fitting clothes and sat in a 'tucked forward' position in order to stay streamlined and reduce drag.

> *Activity:*
>
> *Explanation:*

---

82. (i) Give two examples from two different activities of where you used force to overcome resistance. An example answer is provided.

> *Activity:* Swimming
>
> *Force overcoming resistance:* I used the propulsion from my arm and leg actions to overcome the resistance of the water.

> *Activity 1:*
>
> *Force overcoming resistance:*

> *Activity 2:*
>
> *Force overcoming resistance:*

---

82. (ii) Give two examples from two different activities of where you used resistance to help create force. An example answer is provided.

Activity: Athletics

Example of using resistance to help create force: I used the resistance from the blocks to create force to help me 'sprint start'.

Activity 1:

Example of using resistance to help create force:

Activity 2:

Example of using resistance to help create force:

83. Choose two activities. For the first, explain how a short lever is used for effective performance. For the second, explain how a long lever is used for effective performance. Example answers are provided.

Effective use of short lever

Activity 1: Table tennis

Explanation: Table tennis is a very fast game. You need quick movements and accurate shots. You need to react quickly. You can gain greater control through a short swing and through being quite close to the ball.

Effective use of long lever

Activity 2: Tennis

Explanation: You often need to create power in tennis — for example, when serving and smashing. This is best achieved by a large swing with a straight arm to create a long lever.

Effective use of short lever

Activity 1:

Explanation:

Effective use of long lever

Activity 2:

Explanation:

4. Evaluating Performance

84. Describe the following actions using B.O.S.S. (Body, Order, Shape, Speed). An example answer is provided.

Volleyball – volley

Body:	Relaxed, balanced, open base of support, eyes watching ball closely.
Order:	Run quickly under the ball, adopt steady position, bend arms and legs, play ball in front of forehead with forward and upward stretching movements.
Shape:	Flexed position, bend in joints, extends arms and legs as volley is played.
Speed:	Gentle, controlled speed. Smooth extension of arms and legs.

(i) Gymnastics – forward roll

Body:	
Order:	
Shape:	
Speed:	

84. (ii) Basketball – left-hand lay-up

Body:	
Order:	
Shape:	
Speed:	

(iii) Tennis – backhand

Body:	
Order:	
Shape:	
Speed:	

84. (iv) Gymnastics – handspring

Body:	
Order:	
Shape:	
Speed:	

(v) Gymnastics – neck spring

Body:	
Order:	
Shape:	
Speed:	